THE ALMIGHTY BIBLE

A BIBLICALLY ACCURATE GRAPHIC NOVEL

"The Kingdom of God is at hand!
Repent and believe in the Good News." (1:15)

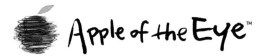

Apple of the Eye Publishing
© 2011 Dakedojo Grace, LLC
All rights reserved.

Available on iTunes for your iPhone and iPad
or visit us online at:

www.thealmightybible.com

Printed in the USA

Produced by Golden Dog, My Legacy Press, and Dakedojo Grace.
Illustrations by Grimsoft Studios supervised by Sara Han-Williams – Pixtrend
Book Design by Poets Road

Foreword

"The beginning of the gospel of Jesus Christ, the Son of God" (1:1), so begins the Gospel of Mark. Although oral testimonies about the life and work of Jesus circulated in abundance from the time of his death and resurrection, the need for written records arose because those who were eyewitnesses reached the end of their lives. Mark is widely recognized as the first Gospel, traditionally understood to be written by John Mark and based on the eyewitness report of the apostle Peter. The date of the Gospel of Mark is thought to coincide with the time of Peter's martyrdom during the reign of the Roman emperor Nero sometime in the mid-60s AD.

The four Gospels (Matthew, Mark, Luke, and John) are all rooted in the real events of the life of Jesus. That said, they are not just interested in reporting mere facts of history. They are vitally concerned about the significance of facts to improve our knowledge of God and relationship with Him. Thus, although the Gospels, particularly the first three (often called Synoptic Gospels), share many similarities, they each highlight certain features about Jesus's story that are relevant to their particular audience. Tradition has it, and it is likely true, that the Gospel of Mark was specifically written for Christians in Rome who were Gentiles. Mark really wants to emphasize to them that Jesus is the Messiah and Son of God and that His death was the ransom that paid for our sins.

Mark is the shortest Gospel by far, and in many ways, it is the most exciting to read. Matthew and Luke start with long genealogies and stories about Jesus's birth, but Mark dives right into Jesus's ministry. Mark gives a sense of urgency to Jesus's work by constantly using the word *immediately* (see 1:10, 1:18, and 1:20 for examples of the Greek word euthys, which is used over 40 times throughout Mark). The action of the gospel story is vivid and presented as if the events are unfolding as they are being narrated. To achieve this effect, the author uses the present tense for verbs, even though he is recording past action.

Jesus's ministry starts in Galilee and its neighborhood (chapters 1–9). His journey to Jerusalem is presented in chapter 10, and the rest of the story is set in Jerusalem (chapters 11–16). The author of Mark often presents topics in blocks. For instance, we find four stories of Jesus casting out demons in 1:21–1:45, five stories of Jesus debating religious leaders in 2:1–3:6, and a number of parables brought together in 4:1–4:34.

The opening verses of Mark set the tone by announcing that its subject is the gospel, or Good News, of Jesus. Jesus is identified as Christ, the Greek word for the Hebrew word Messiah, or anointed one. In the Old Testament, the anointed one was the king, a descendant of David, who sat on the throne and ruled from Jerusalem. God promised David that he would have a descendant sitting on the throne forever (II Samuel 7:11–7:16). However, the last Davidic king to rule from Jerusalem had been removed from the throne by a Babylonian king named Nebuchadnezzar, who then incorporated Judah as a province in his vast empire. Since that time, no Messiah had risen. The faithful began to look to the future for the coming of the Messiah. The message of the Gospel of Mark right from the first verse was that Jesus was that Messiah.

Jesus was also the Son of God (1:1). Before Jesus came, there were many different ideas about what the Messiah would be like. Some thought that he would be a human political or military leader, for instance. Mark announces that Jesus is much more than a mere human king or general; He is the Son of God. In addition, He is the fulfillment of the expectation found in the book of Isaiah and elsewhere of a second exodus, a return from captivity and enslavement (Mark 1:2, Mark 3, Isaiah 40:3, and Malachi 3:1).

Mark then gives brief accounts of Jesus's baptism by John the Baptist (1:4–1:11) and temptations in the wilderness (1:12–1:13) before turning attention to His teaching and actions in Galilee (1:14–9:50). Reading these stories, we are amazed at Jesus's power and authority like those who originally heard His teaching and observed His miracles. The heart of His teaching was that the long-awaited Kingdom of God has arrived. In response, He urges His hearers to repent of their sins and believe the Good News (1:15).

Jesus backs up His claims with acts of power. He shows His authority over the evil spiritual realm by casting demons out of the possessed (1:21–1:28) and healing the sick of their diseases (1:29–1:34). The people declare that they have never heard nor seen anything quite like this before (1:27). Although Jesus tries to keep His identity as the Messiah secret at the beginning of His work (1:24–1:25, 1:34, 7:26, and 8:30), His identity inevitably gets out, and He comes into conflict with the religious authorities. Although their anger toward Him arises in part because of His dramatic acts and growing popularity, it mostly comes from the fact that they suspect that He is making the radical claim that He is none other than God himself. After all, they rightly recognize that He takes actions that only God can do, such as forgiving sins (2:5), announcing lordship over the Sabbath (2:28), and doing away with Old Testament ritual laws concerning food (7:18–7:19).

A turning point of the story takes place in 8:27–9:50 as Jesus prepares to go to Jerusalem. It begins with Peter's acknowledgment that Jesus is the Messiah (8:27–8:30), and then, Jesus, for the first time, predicts His death (8:31–8:33). When Peter strongly rejects this idea, Jesus rebukes him and then teaches that being His disciple involves suffering (8:34–9:1). The story of the Transfiguration, in which Jesus's appearance changed and His clothes became dazzlingly white, anticipates the glory that will come after His suffering.

Chapter 10 narrates the transition from Jesus's ministry in Galilee and the surrounding area to His work in Jerusalem. On His way to Jerusalem, He continues to predict His death, teach, and heal people.

Jesus enters Jerusalem to the ecstatic praise of the crowds (11:1–1:11) but also the resistance of the religious leaders (11:27–1:33). Nonetheless, He continues to teach about a variety of topics, most notably the future (chapter 13)—a passage that anticipates the further development of the book of Revelation.

The end of the Gospel of Mark focuses on Jesus's suffering and death, commonly referred to as the Passion story. Indeed, so much of the end of the Gospel is devoted to the crucifixion that Mark has famously been called a Passion narrative with an extended introduction. Jesus's resurrection is clearly but briefly announced in 16:1–16:8. The emphasis, though, is on His suffering and death because it was His suffering and death that paid the ransom for His follower's sins and provided the model for Christian discipleship.

Mark's story is the foundation of the Christian message. The church is founded on the death and resurrection of Jesus Christ. Alhough written down, for many centuries, people did not read it; they heard it read to them. Whether they read or heard the story, they would see the story in their imaginations or artistic depictions in stained glass, illuminated manuscripts, or paintings. The Almighty Bible has captured our imaginations with a magnificent visual presentation of the story of Jesus, as presented by the Gospel of Mark. Let that story stir and fill you with the amazement that Mark tells us was experienced by the ones who saw Jesus walk and talk on this earth.

Tremper Longman III, PhD

Robert H. Gundry Professor of Biblical Studies
Westmont College

NOTE TO READERS,
PARENTS AND TEACHERS

This is a graphic novelization of Mark. It is not the entire biblical version as we have made edits so that the story is as clear as possible. The text in this book has been edited down from an original public domain translation called the World English Bible which itself was based on a 1904 version of the American Standard Bible. We have edited the text with the best skill we possess and believe that the reader will understand the entire book of the Bible. However, the verse numbers for every page are at the end of the text, allowing for easy reference to the full text in whichever version of the Bible you prefer. Our goal is to encourage young readers to star reading the Bible. Once they do, we don't believe they will ever stop.

Acknowledgements

The Gospel of Mark is an incredible document that everyone should read at least once in his or her life. Regardless of whether you are a devoted Christian, the words and deeds of Jesus are a revelation to all. It is an honor for those of us here at the Almighty Bible to be a part of bringing Mark's Gospel to young people around the world. Our team continues to grow as we are about to send our third book to press. It is only right to let you know who they are and what they do.

Eunice Ahn has done a superb job of supervising the production of this book. Daniel Park and Dr. Joon H. Lee continue to provide business and spiritual support. Dong Chung is most likely on a plane right now making sure that the wheels keep turning and that our company can continue to do its work. Martijn Van Tilborgh is the person who made sure you got this book in your hands. Dan Cordie works tirelessly to spread the Word through the press. Brian Gilson heads up our wonderful customer service team. Reverend Charles Kim helps get our materials into the hands of the kids who need them most. Once again, Dr. Tremper Longman wrote a tremendous foreword that we hope helps provide a context within which to view this book.

We encourage everyone reading this book to also go online and visit our website at www.almightybible.com and review more of the available materials. From mobile apps to the sensational Almighty Bible Club, you will find a new generation of biblical tools for a new generation of kids.

Most of all, we would like to thank those who read our books and then pass the word on to others. So, at the risk of seeming self-serving, we ask you to SPREAD THE WORD!

Kevin O'Donnell

Editor

MARK

MAIN CHARACTERS

JESUS
The Son of God who came to fulfill the Scriptures. He was crucified on the cross and raised to life in three days. He proclaimed that whoever believes in Him will be saved.

JOHN THE BAPTIST
The messenger and prophet sent by God to prepare the way for Christ. He lived in the wilderness and baptized people for the forgiveness of sins.

SIMON PETER
A fisherman of Galilee who was called by Jesus to become a disciple. Jesus named him Peter, meaning *rock*. He was the first to say that Jesus is Christ.

JAMES
As one of the first disciples of Jesus, he was a fisherman who left his father, Zebedee, in order to follow Jesus. Jesus nicknamed James and his brother "Sons of Thunder."

JOHN
The brother of James who was a young fisherman before becoming a disciple. With Peter and James, he witnessed the Transfiguration of Jesus.

MAIN CHARACTERS

JUDAS ISCARIOT
The disciple who went to the chief priests and helped them arrest Jesus. He betrayed Jesus with a kiss.

PHARISEES
An influential religious group that wanted to destroy Jesus. They often questioned Jesus's authority and believed that he spoke blasphemy.

KING HEROD
The ruler of Galilee who ordered the execution of John the Baptist in order to keep his promise to the beautiful daughter of Herodias.

MARY MAGDALENE
A devoted follower of Christ from whom Jesus had cast out seven demons. Jesus appeared to her first after He rose from the dead.

PONTIUS PILATE
The man who authorized the crucifixion of Jesus. He was amazed that Jesus did not defend himself against the chief priests. The crowd ultimately persuaded him to flog and execute Jesus.

MARK

The beginning of the Good News of Jesus Christ, the Son of God. As it written in the prophets, "Behold, I send my messenger before your face, wh will prepare your way before you. The voice of one crying in the wildernes 'Make ready the way of the Lord! Make his paths straight!'" (1:1–1:3)

ohn came baptizing and all the country of Judea went to him. They were
baptized in the Jordan River. John ate locusts and wild honey. He preached,
"After me comes he who is mightier than I, the thong of whose sandals I am
ot worthy to stoop down and loosen. I baptized you in water, but he will
baptize you in the Holy Spirit." (1:4–1:8)

Jesus came from Nazareth of Galilee and was baptized by John in the Jordan. Immediately coming up from the water, he saw the heavens parting and the Spirit descending on him like a dove. A voice came out of the sky, "You are my beloved Son in whom I am well pleased." (1:9–1:11)

Immediately, the Spirit drove him out into the wilderness. He was there in the wilderness forty days tempted by Satan. He was with the wild animals, and the angels were serving him. (1:12–1:13)

Soon thereafter, John was taken into custody. Jesus came into Galilee preaching the Good News of the Kingdom of God, "The time is fulfilled, and the Kingdom of God is at hand! Repent and believe in the Good News." By the Sea of Galilee, Jesus saw Simon and his brother, Andrew, casting a net, for they were fishermen. Jesus said, "Come after me, and I will make you into fishers for men." (1:14–1:17)

They immediately left their nets and followed him. Jesus soon saw James and his brother John, who were also in a boat mending nets. Jesus called to them, and they left their father and went after Jesus. They went into Capernaum, and on the Sabbath day, Jesus entered the synagogue and taught. The people were astonished; for he taught them as if he had direct knowledge of what he said. (1:18–1:22)

A man with an unclean spirit cried out, "Jesus, have you come to destroy us? I know who you are: the Holy One of God!" Jesus rebuked him, "Be quiet, and come out of him!" The unclean spirit cried with a loud voice and came out. The people were amazed. "What is this? A new teaching? He commands unclean spirits, and they obey him!" Jesus's name and deeds spread throughout Galilee. (1:23–1:28)

hey left the synagogue and went into the house of Simon and Andrew.
imon's wife's mother lay sick, and Jesus took her by the hand and raised
er up. The fever left her, and she served them. That evening, people came
> the house, and Jesus healed many who were sick and cast out many
emons. (1:29–1:34)

Early in the morning, while it was still dark, Jesus rose, went out to a deserted place, and prayed there. Simon and those who were with him found him and said, "Everyone is looking for you." Jesus said to them, "Let's go elsewhere into the next towns that I may preach there also because I came out for this reason." He went into the synagogues throughout Galilee, preaching and casting out demons. (1:35–1:39)

A leper came to Jesus and said, "If you want to, you can make me clean." Jesus touched him and said, "I want to. Be made clean." Immediately, the leprosy departed, and the man was made clean. Jesus warned him, "See you say nothing to anybody, but go show yourself to the priest, and offer for your cleansing the things that Moses commanded as proof of your healing." (1:40–1:44)

But the man went out and told everyone, and soon, Jesus could not enter into a city without attracting a huge crowd. He stayed in the desert, and they came to him from everywhere. When he again entered Capernaum, the people came and surrounded the house, and he spoke the word to them. (1:45–2:2)

Four people carried a paralyzed man to see Jesus. When they could not get through the crowd, they removed the roof and lowered the man into the room. Jesus, seeing their faith, said to the paralytic, "Son, your sins are forgiven you." But there were some scribes sitting there thinking, "Why does this man speak blasphemies like that? Who can forgive sins but God alone?" (2:3–2:7)

Jesus, knowing their thoughts, said, "Which is easier: to tell him, 'Your sins are forgiven,' or to say, 'Arise and take up your bed and walk'? But so you know that the Son of Man has authority on earth to forgive sins," he said to the paralytic, "arise and go to your house." The man stood and walked out of the room. Everyone was amazed and glorified God, saying, "We've never seen anything like this!" (2:8–2:12)

Jesus returned to the seaside. People followed, and he taught them. Jesus saw Levi at the tax office, and he said, "Follow me." Levi arose and followed him. Later, at Levi's house, many tax collectors and sinners sat down with Jesus and his disciples. The scribes and Pharisees saw Jesus eating, and they said to his disciples, "Why does he eat with tax collectors and sinners?" (2:13–2:16)

When Jesus heard their words, he said, "Those who are healthy have no need for a physician but those who are sick do. I came not to call the righteous but the sinners to repentance." John's disciples and the Pharisees were fasting, and they came and asked him, "Why do John's disciples and the disciples of the Pharisees fast, but your disciples don't fast?" (2:17–2:18)

Jesus said to them, "Can the groomsmen fast while the bridegroom is with them? But the days will come when the bridegroom will be taken away, and then, they will fast. No one sews a piece of unshrunk cloth on an old garment or else the patch shrinks, and the new tears away from the old, and a worse hole is made. No one puts new wine into old wineskins or else the new wine will burst the skins." (2:19–2:22)

16

Jesus was walking through fields on the Sabbath as his disciples ate th[e] grain. The Pharisees said, "Why do they do such unlawful things?" Jesu[s] said, "Did you never read what David did when he was hungry? How h[e] entered God's house and ate the holy bread and shared it with those wi[th] him? The Sabbath was made for man, not man for the Sabbath. The Son [of] Man is lord even of the Sabbath." (2:23–2:28)

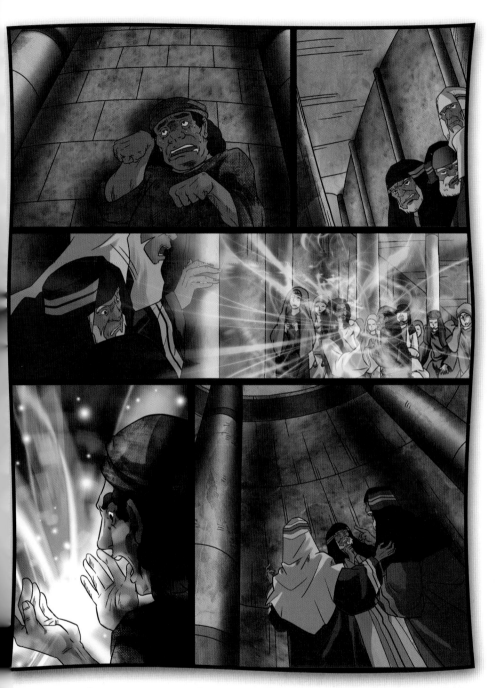

Jesus entered a synagogue where a man with a withered hand sat. The Pharisees watched to see if Jesus would heal him on the Sabbath. Jesus said to them, "Is it lawful on the Sabbath to do good or to do harm?" But they were silent. Jesus grieved at their heartlessness and said to the man, "Stretch out your hand." He stretched it out. The Pharisees left and conspired with others against Jesus. (3:1–3:6)

Jesus withdrew to the sea, and a great multitude followed. He asked hi[s] disciples to bring a boat, so he could sit on it as he spoke. For he ha[d] healed so many people that everyone suffering wanted to touch him. Thos[e] possessed by unclean spirits fell down before him and cried, "You are th[e] Son of God!" Jesus sternly warned them that they should not make hi[m] known. (3:7–3:12)

Jesus climbed a mountain and called twelve to be with him and to preach and to have the authority to heal sicknesses and to cast out demons: Simon, whom he gave the name Peter; James, son of Zebedee; John, brother of James; Andrew; Philip; Bartholomew; Matthew; Thomas; James, son of Alphaeus; Thaddaeus; Simon the Zealot; and Judas Iscariot, who betrayed him. (3:13–3:19)

Scribes from Jerusalem said, "By the prince of the demons, he casts out the demons." Jesus replied to them in parables, "How can Satan cast out Satan? If a kingdom is divided against itself, that kingdom cannot stand. Nor may a house divided stand. If Satan has risen up against himself and is divided, he can't stand and has an end. I tell you, all sins of the descendants of man will be forgiven, but whoever blasphemes the Holy Spirit never has forgiveness." (3:20–3:30)

A crowd was sitting around Jesus, and they told him, "Behold, your mother, your brothers, and your sisters are outside looking for you." He answered them, "Who are my mother and my brothers?" Looking at those around him, he said, "Behold, my mother and my brothers! For whoever does the will of God, the same is my brother and my sister and mother." (3:32–3:35)

Jesus often taught in parables, "Listen! A farmer went out to sow his field. Some seeds fell by the road, and birds ate it. Others fell on the rocky ground where they immediately sprouted because the soil was shallow, but nearly rootless, they withered. Others fell by thorns and choked. Others fell into good ground and yielded fruit. Some brought forth thirty times, some sixty times, and some one hundred times as much." He said, "Whoever has ear to hear, let him hear." (4:2–4:9)

When they were alone, the disciples asked Jesus about the parables, and
he said, "Don't you understand? The farmer sows the word. The ones by the
road are the ones who when they have heard, Satan immediately comes and
takes away the word. Those who are sown on the rocky places, immediately
receive it with joy, but when oppression or persecution arises because of the
word, they stumble." (4:10–4:17)

"Others are those who are sown among the thorns. These are those who have heard the word, and the cares of this age and the deceitfulness of riches and the lusts of other things entering in choke the word, and it becomes unfruitful. Those which were sown on the good ground are those who hear the word and accept it and bear fruit: some thirty times, some sixty times, and some one hundred times." (4:18–4:20)

Jesus said to them, "Is the lamp to be put under a basket or a bed? Isn't it put on a stand? For there is nothing hidden, except that it should be made known; neither was anything made secret but that it should come to light. If any man has ears to hear, let him hear." He said to them, "With whatever measure you measure, it will be measured to you, and more will be given to you who hear." (4:21–4:24)

"For whoever has, to him will more be given, and he who doesn't have, even that which he has will be taken away. The Kingdom of God is as if a man should cast seed on the earth and then just sleep and rise night and day; though he knows not how, the seed should spring up and grow. For the earth bears fruit: first the blade, then the ear, then the full grain in the ear. But when the fruit is ripe, immediately, he puts forth the sickle because the harvest has come." (4:25–4:29)

Jesus said, "With what parable will we explain the Kingdom of God? It's like a mustard seed that, though it is smaller than all the other seeds, grows greater than all the herbs and puts out great branches, so that the birds can lodge under its shadow." With many such parables, he spoke the word to them. (4:30–4:33)

That evening, they set sail, but a storm arose, waves beat the boat, and it began to sink. They awoke Jesus, "Teacher, don't you care that we are dying?" Jesus immediately rebuked the wind saying, "Peace! Be still!" The wind ceased, and there was a great calm. He said, "Why are you so afraid and have no faith?" They said to one another, "Who then is this that ever the wind and the sea obey him?" (4:35–4:41)

They came to the other side of the sea, into the country of the Gadarenes.
Jesus came out of the boat, and a man with an unclean spirit came out of
the tombs where he lived. Nobody could bind him any more, not even with
chains, because the chains had been torn apart by him. Nobody had the
strength to tame this man. (5:1–5:4)

Always, night and day, he was crying out and cutting himself. When h saw Jesus from afar, he ran and bowed down to him. Crying out with a lou voice, he said, "What have I to do with you, Jesus, you Son of the Most Hig God? Don't torment me." Jesus said, "Come out of the man, you unclea spirit!" Jesus asked the spirit, "What is your name?" He said to him, "M name is Legion, for we are many." (5:5–5:9)

On the mountainside, there was a herd of pigs. The demons begged Jesus, "Send us into the pigs." Jesus gave them permission. The unclean spirits came out and entered the pigs. The herd of about two thousand rushed down the steep bank, and they were drowned in the sea. Those who tended to the pigs fled and told it in the city and in the country. The people came to see what had happened. (5:10–5:14)

They saw the previously possessed man, clothed and in his right mind, and they were afraid. They begged Jesus to depart from their region. As Jesus entered the boat, the man who had been possessed begged Jesus to take him. Instead, Jesus said, "Go to your friends and tell them what great things the Lord has done for you and how he had mercy on you." He did so, and everyone marveled. (5:15–5:20)

When Jesus had crossed back over in the boat to the other side, a great multitude was gathered to him. One of the rulers of the synagogue, Jairus, came, and seeing Jesus, he fell at his feet, saying, "My little daughter is at the point of death. Please come and lay your hands on her that she may be made healthy and live." (5:21–5:23)

Jesus went with him, and a great multitude followed, pressing upon him on
sides. A woman who had been bleeding for years, having heard about Jesu
came up behind him in the crowd and touched his clothes. For she said, "If I j
touch his clothes, I will be made well." Immediately, she felt that she was heal
of her affliction. (5:24–5:29)

sus, perceiving that power had gone out from him, turned and asked,
"Who touched my clothes?" His disciples said to him, "You see the multitude
ressing against you, and you say, 'Who touched me?'" The woman, fearing
nd trembling, came and fell down before him and told him all the truth. He
aid to her, "Daughter, your faith has made you well. Go in peace and be
ured of your disease." (5:30–5:34)

Soon thereafter, people came from Jairus's house saying, "Your daughter
dead. There is no use in bothering the Teacher any more." But Jesus said
Jairus, "Don't be afraid, only believe." He allowed no one to follow, exce
Peter, James, and John. People at Jairus's house were weeping, but Jes
said to them, "Why do you make an uproar and weep? The child is not de
but is asleep." (5:35–5:39)

...he people there ridiculed Jesus, but Jesus just told them to leave, and he took ...airus, the child's mother, and his disciples and went in where the child was ...ing. He took her hand, and said, "Girl, I tell you, get up!" Immediately, the ...irl rose up and walked. Everyone was amazed, but Jesus strictly ordered ...em to tell no one and commanded that something should be given to her ...eat. (5:40–5:43)

Jesus went to his own country, Nazareth, with his disciples. On the Sabbath he taught in the synagogue, and many were astonished, saying, "Where did this man get these things," and "How can such mighty works come about by his hands? Isn't this the carpenter, the son of Mary and brother of James, Joses, Judah, and Simon? Aren't his sisters here with us?" They were offended by him. (6:1–6:3)

esus said to them, "A prophet is not without honor, except in his own country nd among his own relatives and in his own house." He could do no mighty ork there, except that he laid his hands on a few sick people and healed em. He marveled because of their unbelief. He went around the villages aching. (6:4–6:6)

Jesus sent out the twelve disciples two by two and gave them authority ov
the unclean spirits. He commanded them that they should take nothing exce
a staff, saying, "Whoever will not receive nor hear you, shake off the du
under your feet as you leave. It will be better for Sodom and Gomorrﾄ
on judgment day than for that city!" They went and preached that peop
should repent. They cast out demons, anointed the sick, and healed mar
(6:7–6:13)

41

ng Herod heard this, for Jesus's name had become known, and he said,
ohn the Baptizer has risen from the dead, and therefore, these powers are
work in him." But others said, "He is Elijah." And still others said, "He is
e of the prophets." But Herod said, "This is John, whom I beheaded, risen
om the dead." (6:14–6:16)

For Herod had arrested John for the sake of Herodias, his brother Philip
former wife, whom he married upon her divorce from Phillip. Herodias ha
wanted John killed because John had told Herod, "It is not lawful for yc
to have your brother's wife." However, Herod feared John, knowing th
he was a righteous and holy man, and allowed no harm to come to him
prison. (6:17–6:20)

Then, while John was in prison, Herod had a celebration for his own birthday. Herodias's daughter danced beautifully for Herod and his guests. The king said to the young lady, "Ask me whatever you want, and I will give it to you." He swore to her, "Whatever you shall ask of me, I will give you." (6:21–6:23)

She first went to her mother. "What shall I ask for?" Herodias said, "The head of John the Baptizer." She returned to the king, saying, "I want the head of John the Baptizer on a platter." The king was sad, but he sent out a soldier who beheaded John in the prison and returned with his head on a platter. When John's disciples heard this, they came and took up his corpse and laid it in a tomb. (6:24–6:29)

The apostles returned to Jesus and told him all they had done and taught. He said to them, "Let us go to a deserted place and rest awhile." For there were so many people coming and going that they had no time to even eat. They went by boat to a deserted place, but the people saw them going and ran, so that the multitudes arrived before the boat had even landed. (6:30–6:33)

Jesus saw the huge crowd, and he had compassion on them because they were like sheep without a shepherd, and he began to teach them many things. When it was late in the day, his disciples came to him and said, "This place is deserted, and it is late in the day. Send them away that they may go into the surrounding country and villages and buy themselves bread; for they have nothing to eat." (6:34-6:36)

ut Jesus said to them, "How many loaves do you have? Go see." They said,
Five loaves and two fish." Jesus commanded them that everyone should sit
own on the green grass in groups of hundreds and fifties. (6:38–6:40)

Jesus took the loaves and fish, looked up to heaven, blessed and broke the loaves, and gave the bread to his disciples to set before the people. Then, he divided the two fish among them all. Everyone ate and was filled. Afterwards, they gathered twelve baskets full of leftover bread and fish. Those who ate were five thousand men. (6:41–6:44)

Immediately, Jesus made his disciples get into the boat and go to the other side of the Sea of Galilee, to Bethsaida, while he himself sent the multitude away. After he had taken leave of them, he went up the mountain to pray. When evening had come, the boat was in the midst of the sea, and Jesus was alone on the land. (6:45–6:47)

The wind began blowing, and his disciples' boat was in distress. Jesus came to them, walking on the sea. They thought it was a ghost and cried out in fear. But Jesus said to them, "Cheer up! It is I! Don't be afraid." He got into the boat with them, and the wind ceased. They were very amazed; for they hadn't fully learned from the loaves, and their minds were slow to understand Jesus's power. (6:48–6:52)

They landed at Gennesaret, and the people immediately recognized Jesus. Wherever Jesus and his disciples went, the people laid the sick in the marketplaces and begged that they might touch just the fringe of his garment, and as they did, they were made well. (6:53–6:56)

Then, the Pharisees and some of the scribes from Jerusalem came to se
Jesus. When they saw some of his disciples eating bread with unwashe
hands, they found fault. (For the Pharisees and the Jews don't eat unless the
wash their hands and forearms, holding to these and many other tradition
of their elders.) (7:1–7:4)

The Pharisees asked Jesus, "Why do your disciples eat their bread with unwashed hands?" Jesus answered them, "Isaiah prophesied well when he wrote of you hypocrites, 'This people honors me with their lips, but their heart is far from me. But in vain do they worship me, teaching as doctrines the commandments of men.'" (7:5–7:7)

"For you set aside the commandment of God and hold tightly to the traditions of men." He called all the multitude to himself and said to them, "Hear me, all of you, and understand. There is nothing from outside of the man that going into him can defile him, but the things that proceed out of the man are those that defile the man. If anyone has ears to hear, let him hear!" (7:8–7:16)

When he had entered into a house away from the multitude, his disciples asked him about the parable. He said to them, "Are you thus without understanding also? Don't you perceive that whatever goes into the man from outside can't defile him because it doesn't go into his heart but into his stomach, then into the latrine, thus, purifying all foods?" (7:17–7:19)

He said, "That which proceeds out of the man, that defiles the man. For fro[m] within, out of the hearts of men, proceed evil thoughts, adulteries, sexu[al] sins, murders, thefts, covetings, wickedness, deceit, lustful desires, an ev[il] eye, blasphemy, pride, and foolishness. All these evil things come fro[m] within and defile the man." (7:20–7:23)

Jesus traveled to the borders of Tyre and Sidon. He entered a house and didn't want anyone to know, but a Greek woman whose little daughter had an unclean spirit came and fell down at his feet. She begged him that he would cast the demon out of her daughter. But Jesus said to her, "Let the children be filled first; for it is not appropriate to take the children's bread and throw it to the dogs." (7:24–7:27)

But she answered him, "Yes, Lord. Yet, even the dogs under the table eat th[e] children's crumbs." He said to her, "For this saying, go your way. The demo[n] has gone out of your daughter." She went away and found her child on th[e] bed, with the demon gone. Jesus departed Tyre and Sidon and came to th[e] Sea of Galilee via the region of Decapolis. (7:28–7:31)

They brought a man to Jesus who was deaf and had a speech impediment. They begged him to lay his hand on him. Jesus took the man aside from the multitude. He put his fingers into his ears and then spat and touched the man's tongue. Looking up to heaven, Jesus sighed and said, "Be opened!" 7:32–7:34)

Immediately, the man's ears were opened, and the impediment of his tongue was released, and he spoke clearly. Jesus commanded them to tell no one but the more he commanded, the more widely they proclaimed his works. The people were astonished, saying, "He makes even the deaf hear and the mute speak!" (7:35–7:37)

n those days, when there was a very great multitude, and they had nothing to eat, Jesus called his disciples to himself and said to them, "I have compassion on the multitude because they have stayed with me now three days and have nothing to eat. If I send them away fasting to their home, they will faint on the way; for some of them have come a long way." (8:1–8:3)

His disciples answered him, "From where could one satisfy these people with bread here in this deserted place?" He asked them, "How many loaves do you have?" They said, "Seven." Jesus commanded the multitude to sit down on the ground, and he took the seven loaves. Having given thanks, he broke them and gave them to his disciples to serve to the multitude. (8:4–8:6)

...ey had a few small fish. Having blessed them, he said to serve them. They ...e and were filled. They took up seven baskets of broken pieces that were ...t over. Those who had eaten were about four thousand. Then, he sent them ...vay. Immediately, he entered into the boat with his disciples and sailed to ...e region of Dalmanutha. (8:7–8:10)

The Pharisees came and questioned Jesus, seeking a sign from heav[en] and testing him. He sighed deeply in his spirit and said, "Why does th[is] generation seek a sign? Most certainly, I tell you no sign will be given to th[is] generation." He left them and, again entering into the boat, departed to [the] other side. They forgot to take bread, and they didn't have more than o[ne] loaf in the boat with them. (8:11–8:14)

...us warned them, saying, "Take heed; beware of the yeast of the Pharisees ... the yeast of Herod." They voiced their conclusion as to why he spoke of ...st. "It's because we have no bread." Jesus, perceiving it, said to them, "Why ... you reason that it's because you have no bread? Don't you understand? ...ving eyes, don't you see? Having ears, don't you hear?" (8:15–8:18)

"Don't you remember? When I broke the five loaves among the five thousand how many baskets full of broken pieces did you take up?" They told him "Twelve." "When the seven loaves fed the four thousand, how many baskets full of broken pieces did you take up?" They told him, "Seven." He asked them "Don't you understand yet?" (8:18–8:21)

Jesus came to Bethsaida. They brought a blind man to him and begged Jesus to touch him. He took hold of the blind man by the hand and brought him out of the village. When he had spit on his eyes and laid his hands on him, he asked him if he saw anything. He looked up and said, "I see men; I see them like trees walking." (8:22–8:24)

Jesus again laid his hands on the man's eyes, and he saw everyone clear[ly].
Jesus sent him away, saying, "Don't tell anyone." Jesus went out with [his]
disciples to Caesarea Philippi. On the way, he asked his disciples, "W[ho]
do men say that I am?" They told him, "John the Baptizer, Elijah, or one [of]
the prophets." Jesus said to them, "But who do you say that I am?" Pe[ter]
answered, "You are the Christ." (8:25–8:29)

Jesus told them that the Son of Man must suffer many things and be rejected by the elders, chief priests, and scribes. Then, he would be killed and after three days rise again. He spoke to them openly. Peter took him and began to rebuke him. But turning around and seeing his disciples, Jesus rebuked Peter, "Get behind me, Satan! For you have in mind not the things of God but the things of men." (8:30–8:33)

Jesus called the multitude to himself and said, "Whoever wants to come afte[r] me, let him deny himself and take up his cross and follow me. For whoeve[r] wants to save his life will lose it, and whoever will lose his life for my sak[e] and the sake of the Good News will save it. For what does it profit a man t[o] gain the whole world and forfeit his life?" (8:34–8:36)

or what will a man give in exchange for his life? For whoever will be
ashamed of me and of my words, the Son of Man also will be ashamed
him when he comes in the glory of his Father with the holy angels. Most
certainly, I tell you, there are some standing here who will not taste death
til they see the Kingdom of God come with power." (8:37–9:1)

After six days, Jesus took Peter, James, and John and brought them up on a high mountain, and he was changed into another form in front of them. His clothing became glistening, exceedingly white like snow, such as a launderer on earth can whiten them. Elijah and Moses appeared to them, and they were talking with Jesus. (9:2–9:4)

eter spoke to Jesus, "Rabbi, let's make three tents: one for you, one for oses, and one for Elijah." For he didn't know what else to say; for they ere very afraid. A cloud came overshadowing them, and a voice came t of the cloud, "This is my beloved Son. Listen to him." Suddenly, looking ound, they saw no one with them any more, except Jesus only. (9:5–9:8)

As they were coming down from the mountain, Jesus commanded them th
they should tell no one what things they had seen until after the Son of M
had risen from the dead. They spoke amongst themselves, questioning wh
the "rising from the dead" meant. They asked Jesus a question, "Why do th
scribes say that Elijah must come first?" (9:9–9:11)

Jesus answered, "Elijah indeed comes first and restores all things. But I tell you that Elijah has come, and they have also done to him whatever they wanted to, even as it is written." Coming back to the disciples, Jesus saw a great multitude around them and scribes questioning them. As soon as the people saw Jesus coming, they ran to greet him. (9:12–9:15)

One of the multitude said, "Teacher, I brought to you my son who has a mute spirit, and wherever it seizes him, it throws him down, and he foams at the mouth and grinds his teeth and wastes away. I asked your disciples to cast it out, and they weren't able." Jesus answered, "Unbelieving generation, how long shall I be with you? How long shall I bear with you? Bring him to me." (9:16–9:19)

They brought the boy, and when he saw Jesus, the spirit inside caused him to fall, wallowing and foaming at the mouth. Jesus asked the father, "How long has this been happening to him?" The man said, "From childhood. Please have compassion on us, and help us." Jesus said to him, "If you can believe, all things are possible to him who believes." (9:20–9:23)

Immediately, the man cried out with tears, "I believe. Help my unbelief!"
Jesus then rebuked the unclean spirit, "I command you, come out of him
and never enter him again!" Crying and convulsing, the spirit came out o
him. The boy lay on the ground motionless, and some people thought he
was dead. But Jesus took him by the hand and raised him up, and the bo
awakened. (9:24–9:27)

When they were alone, his disciples asked, "Why couldn't we cast it out?"
...sus said, "This kind can come out only through prayer and fasting." And
...sus said, "The Son of Man is being handed over to the hands of men,
...d they will kill him, and when he is killed, on the third day, he will rise
...gain." But they didn't understand the saying and were afraid to ask him.
...:28–9:32)

80

In Capernaum, Jesus asked his disciples, "What were you arguing about o
the way?" They were ashamed; for they'd argued over which of them wo
greater. Jesus said, "He who would be first, shall be last, servant of all." H
took a child in his arms and said to them, "Whoever receives one such litt
child in my name receives me, and whoever receives me doesn't receive m
but him who sent me." (9:33–9:37)

John said, "Teacher, we saw someone who doesn't follow us casting out demons in your name, and we forbade him." But Jesus said, "Don't forbid him; for there is no one who will do a mighty work in my name and be able quickly to speak evil of me. For whoever is not against us is on our side. Whoever gives you a cup of water in my name, because you are Christ's, he will be rewarded." (9:38–9:41)

"Whoever will cause one of these little ones who believe in me to stumble, would be better for him if he were thrown into the sea with a millstone hun around his neck. If your hand causes you to stumble, cut it off. It is better fc you to enter into life maimed rather than having your two hands to go int Gehenna, into the unquenchable fire where their worm doesn't die, and th fire is not quenched." (9:42–9:48)

Jesus arose from there and went to Judea and beyond the Jordan River. Multitudes came together to him again, and he began teaching them. The Pharisees, testing him, asked, "Is it lawful for a man to divorce his wife?" Jesus answered, "What did Moses command you?" They said, "Moses allowed a certificate of divorce to be written and to divorce her." (10:1–10:4)

But Jesus said to them, "For your hardness of heart, he wrote you thi
commandment. But from the beginning of the creation, God made ther
male and female. For this cause, a man will leave his father and mother and
will join to his wife, and the two will become one flesh, so that they are n
longer two but one flesh." (10:5–10:8)

'What, therefore, God has joined together, let no man separate." In the house, his disciples asked him again about the same matter. He said to them, "Whoever divorces his wife and marries another commits adultery against her. If a woman herself divorces her husband and marries another, she commits adultery." (10:9–10:12)

One day, people were bringing little children to Jesus, so he could touch them, but the disciples stopped them. Jesus said, "Let the children come to me; for the Kingdom of God belongs to such as these. Whoever will not receive the Kingdom of God like a little child, he will in no way enter into it." Jesus took the children in his arms and blessed them, laying his hands on them. (10:13–10:16)

man knelt, saying, "Good Teacher, what must I do for eternal life?" Jesus
id, "Good? No one is good except God. Follow the commandments." "I
ave," said the man. Jesus looked into him, "Go, sell everything, and give
the poor, and you will have treasure in heaven, and come follow me,
king up the cross." But the man's face fell; for he was rich. Jesus said to
s disciples, "How difficult it is for those who have riches to enter into the
ngdom of God!" (10:17–10:23)

The disciples were shocked. Jesus answered again, "Children, how hard it for those who trust in riches to enter into the Kingdom of God! It is easi for a camel to go through a needle's eye than for a rich man to enter in the Kingdom of God." They were astonished, saying, "Then who can saved?" Jesus, said, "With men, it is impossible but not with God; for things are possible with God." (10:24–10:27)

eter began to tell him, "Behold, we have left all and have followed you."
sus said, "There is no one who has left house or brothers or sisters or father
mother or wife or children or land for my sake and for the sake of the
ood News who will not receive one hundred times more now in this time—
uses, brothers, sisters, mothers, children, and land—with persecutions and
the age to come eternal life. But many who are first will be last and the
st first." (10:28–10:31)

On the way to Jerusalem, Jesus again told the twelve disciples the things th
were going to happen to him. "Behold, we are going up to Jerusalem. T
Son of Man will be delivered to the chief priests and the scribes. They w
condemn him to death and will deliver him to the Gentiles. They will mo
him, spit on him, scourge him, and kill him. On the third day, he will ri
again." (10:32–10:34)

ames and John came to Jesus and asked for a favor. Jesus said to them,
"What do you want me to do for you?" They said to him, "Grant to us that
we may sit, one at your right hand and one at your left hand, in your glory."
But Jesus said to them, "You don't know what you are asking. Are you able
to drink the cup that I drink and to be baptized with the baptism that I am
baptized with?" (10:35–10:38)

They said to him, "We are able." Jesus said to them, "You shall indeed drink the cup that I drink, and you shall be baptized with the baptism that I am baptized with, but to sit at my right hand and at my left hand is not mine to give but for whom it has been prepared." When the others heard, they became upset with James and John. (10:39–10:41)

esus summoned them and said, "Whoever of you wants to become first mong you shall be the servant of all. For the Son of Man also came not to e served but to serve and to give his life as a ransom for many." (10:42– 0:45)

As Jesus was leaving Jericho with his disciples and a great multitud Bartimaeus, a blind beggar, was sitting by the road. When he heard th it was Jesus the Nazarene, he began to cry out and say, "Jesus, you son David, have mercy on me!" Many rebuked him that he should be quiet, b he cried out again. (10:46–10:48)

sus stood still and asked him, "What do you want me to do for you?" The ~~bl~~ind man said to him, "Rabboni, that I may see again." Jesus said to him, ~~"~~Go your way. Your faith has made you well." Immediately, he received his ~~si~~ght and followed Jesus in the way. (10:49–10:52)

They came to the Mount of Olives, and Jesus told two of his disciples, "C
into the streets. You will find a donkey. Untie him and bring him. If anyo
asks you, 'Why,' say, 'The Lord needs him.'" They did as Jesus said, and Jes
sat on the donkey as he rode into Jerusalem. Many spread their garments
the way, and others cut down branches from the trees and spread them
the road. (11:1–11:8)

People cried out, "Hosanna! Blessed is he who comes in the name of the
Lord! Blessed is the kingdom of our father, David! Hosanna in the highest!"
Jesus entered into the temple in Jerusalem. When he had looked around at
everything, it being now evening, he went out to Bethany with the twelve.
(11:9–11:11)

The next day, Jesus was hungry. Seeing a fig tree afar off, he came to see
perhaps he might find fruit on it. But he found nothing but leaves; for it wa
not the season for figs. Jesus told it, "May no one ever eat fruit from yo
again," and his disciples heard his words. (11:12–11:14)

ey came to Jerusalem, and Jesus entered into the temple and began to
row out those who bought and sold things in the temple. He overthrew the
bles of the money changers and the seats of those who sold doves. He
ught the people there, saying, "Isn't it written, 'My house will be called a
use of prayer for all the nations?' But you have made it a den of robbers!"
1:15–11:17)

The chief priests and the scribes heard of what Jesus had done in the tem
and discussed ways they could destroy him. For they feared Jesus beca
all the multitude was astonished at his teaching. When evening came, Je
left the city. (11:18–11:19)

n the morning, Peter said, "Look. The tree you cursed has died." Jesus said,
Have faith in God. For whoever tells this mountain, 'Be taken up and cast
ito the sea,' and believes in his heart that it is happening, it shall be so.
Vhatever you pray and ask for, believe that you have received them and so
ou shall. When you pray, forgive others, so that your Father in heaven may
lso forgive you." (11:20–11:26)

The chief priests and the scribes and the elders came to Jesus, saying to him,
"By what authority do you do these things? Or who gave you this authority
to do these things?" Jesus said to them, "I will ask you one question. Answer
me, and I will tell you by what authority I do these things. The baptism of
John—was it from heaven or from men? Answer me." (11:27–11:30)

...1ey reasoned with themselves, "If we should say, 'From heaven,' he will ...1y, 'Why then did you not believe him?' If we should say, 'From men,'" they ...ared the people; for all held John to really be a prophet. They answered ...sus, "We don't know." Jesus said to them, "Then neither do I tell you by ...hat authority I do these things." (11:31–11:33)

Jesus then told them a parable. "A man planted a vineyard, rented it out
a farmer, and went into another country. Later, he sent a servant to get fr
the farmer his share of the fruit. He was beaten and sent away empty. T
farmer sent another servant, and they threw stones at him and sent him aw
shamefully. He sent another, and they killed him and many others, beati
some and killing some." (12:1–12:5)

nally, he sent his son, saying, 'They will respect my son.' But the farmers
d, 'This is the heir, kill him, and the inheritance will be ours.' They killed
n." Jesus then said, "What will the lord of the vineyard do? He will come
d destroy the farmers and give the vineyard to others. Haven't you read
s Scripture: 'The stone which the builders rejected, the same was made the
d of the corner'?" (12:6–12:10)

The scribes and elders left but sent some of the Pharisees to trap Jesus w
words. They asked, "Teacher, we know that you are honest and teach t
way of God. Is it lawful to pay taxes to Caesar? Shall we give, or shall v
not give?" Jesus, knowing their hypocrisy, said, "Why do you test me? Bri
me a denarius that I may see it." (12:12–12:15)

They brought it, and Jesus said, "Whose is this image and inscription?" They said to him, "Caesar's." Jesus answered, "Render to Caesar the things that are Caesar's and to God the things that are God's." They marveled greatly at him. (12:16–12:17)

Then Sadducees came to try and trap Jesus. They said, "There were seven brothers. The first took a wife and, dying, left no offspring. The second took her and died, leaving no children behind him. The third likewise, and the seven took her and left no children. Last of all, the woman also died. In the resurrection, when they rise, whose wife will she be of them? For the seven had her as a wife." (12:18–12:23)

Jesus answered, "Not knowing the Scriptures nor the power of God, you are mistaken. When they rise, they neither marry nor are given in marriage but are like angels in heaven. But about the dead that they are raised, haven't you read in the book of Moses about the bush, how God spoke to him, saying, 'I am the God of Abraham, the God of Isaac, and the God of Jacob'? He is not the God of the dead but of the living. You are therefore badly mistaken." (12:24–12:27)

A scribe, knowing that Jesus had answered them well, then asked, "Whic[h] commandment is the greatest?" Jesus said, "The greatest is, 'Hear, Israel, th[e] Lord our God. You shall love the Lord your God with all your heart and wit[h] all your soul and with all your mind and with all your strength.' This is the fir[st] commandment. The second most important is, 'You shall love your neighb[or] as yourself.'" (12:28–12:31)

The scribe said, "Truly, teacher, you have said well that there is none other but he, and to love him with all of one's heart, understanding, soul, and strength and to love his neighbor as himself is more important than all the burnt offerings and sacrifices." Jesus saw that he answered wisely and said, "You are not far from the Kingdom of God." No one dared ask him any question after that. (12:32–12:34)

Jesus continued to teach, "Why do scribes say that the Christ is the son of David? David himself said, 'The Lord said to my Lord, "Sit at my right hand."' David himself calls him Lord, so how can the Christ be his son?" The common people smiled as he continued, "Beware of scribes in long robes who get greetings in the marketplaces and the best seats in the synagogues and at feasts but devour widows' houses as they make long prayers. They will be condemned." (12:35-12:40)

Jesus sat down opposite the treasury and saw how the multitude cast money into the treasury. Many who were rich gave much. A poor widow came, and she cast in two small brass coins. Jesus called to his disciples and said, "This poor widow gave more than all those who gave much out of their abundance, but she, out of her poverty, gave all that she had to live on." (12:41–12:44)

Leaving the temple, Jesus said, "Do you see these great buildings? There will not be left here one stone, which will not be thrown down." As they sat on the Mount of Olives opposite the temple, Peter, James, John, and Andrew asked, "When will these things be? What is the sign that they are all about to be fulfilled?" Jesus answered, "Be careful that no one leads you astray. For many will come in my name, saying, 'I am he.'" (13:1–13:6)

When you hear of wars and rumors of wars, don't be troubled. For those must happen, but the end is not yet. For nation will rise against nation and ngdom against kingdom. There will be earthquakes in various places. There ill be famines and troubles. These things are the beginning of birth pains. It watch yourselves; for they will deliver you up to councils." (13:7–13:9)

"You will be beaten in synagogues. You will stand before rulers and king[ ] for my sake, for a testimony to them. The Good News must first be preach[ ] to all the nations. When they lead you away and deliver you up, don't [ ] anxious beforehand or premeditate what you will say, but say whatever w[ ] be given you in that hour. For it is not you who speak but the Holy Spiri[ ] (13:9–13:11)

Brother will give up his brother to death and the father his child. Children will rise against parents. You will be hated by all for my name's sake, but he who endures, will be saved. But when you see the abomination of desolation spoken of by Daniel, then let those in Judea flee to the mountains, and let him who is on the housetop not go down nor enter in to take anything out of his house." (13:12–13:15)

"Let those in the field not return for their cloak. Woe to those who are with child or nurse babies! Pray that your flight won't be in the winter. For in those days, there will be oppression greater than any since the beginning of God's creation, and never will be again. No flesh would have been saved, except that for the sake of his chosen ones, he shortened the days. In this time, if anyone tells you, 'Look, here is the Christ,' don't believe it." (13:16–13:21)

False christs and prophets will show signs and wonders that may lead astray
ven the chosen ones, though I have told you all things beforehand. The sun
ill be darkened, the moon will not shine, the stars will be falling from the
ky, and the powers in heaven will be shaken. Then, they will see the Son
f Man coming in clouds with great power and glory. His angels will gather
is chosen ones from the four winds, from the ends of the earth to the ends
f the sky." (13:22–13:27)

"Just as when the fig tree's branch puts forth leaves, you know summer
near; so also when you see these things, know that it is near. I say to you
this generation will not pass away until all these things happen. Heaven an
earth will pass away, but my words will not pass away. But of that day o
hour, no one knows, not the angels nor the Son but only the Father. Watc
keep alert, and pray." (13:28–13:33)

... is like a man traveling to another country, having left his house and ...ven authority to his servants and to each one his work and commanded ... doorkeeper to keep watch. Watch, therefore, for you don't know when ... lord of the house is coming, whether at evening or at midnight or in the ...orning; lest coming, suddenly he might find you sleeping. What I tell you, ...ell all: watch." (13:34–13:37)

Two days before Passover, the chief priests plotted ways to seize Jesus and kill him, nervously saying, "Not during the feast, or people may riot." While he was at Bethany in the house of Simon, the leper, a woman came with an alabaster jar of expensive ointment, which she poured over his head. But some grumbled, "Why did she waste this ointment and not sell it to give the money to the poor?" (14:1–14:5)

ut Jesus said, "She has done a good work for me. You shall always have the
oor, so that you may do them good, but you will not always have me. She
as done what she could and anointed my body beforehand for the burying.
Most certainly, wherever this Good News may be preached throughout the
world, the good works of this woman will also be spoken of." (14:6–14:9)

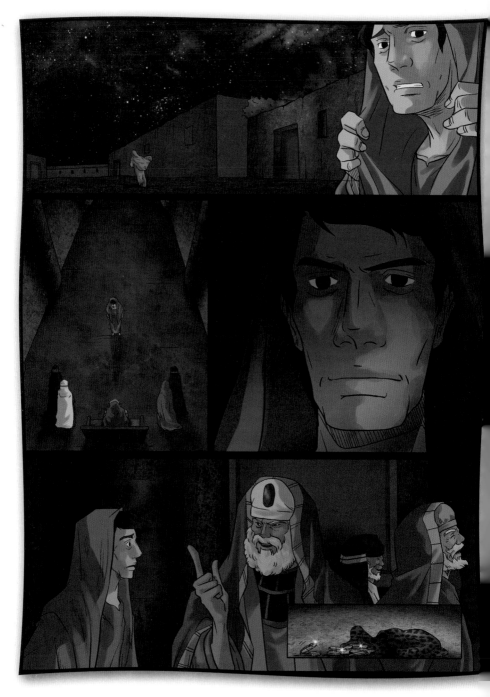

Judas Iscariot, who was one of the twelve disciples, went away to the chief priests that he might betray and deliver Jesus to them. When they heard it they were glad and promised to give him money. They discussed how and where he could deliver Jesus to them. (14:10–14:11)

On the first day of unleavened bread, Jesus said to two of his disciples, "Go into the city, and there you will meet a man carrying a pitcher of water. Follow him, and wherever he enters in, tell the master of the house, 'The Teacher says, "Where is the guest room where I may eat the Passover with my disciples?"' He will show you a large upper room. Get ready for us here." (14:12–14:15)

That evening as they were eating, Jesus said, "One of you will betray me—he who eats with me." They sorrowfully asked him one by one, "Surely no I?" And Jesus said, "It is one of the twelve; he who dips with me in the dish For the Son of Man goes, even as it is written about him, but woe to that ma by whom the Son of Man is betrayed! It would be better for that man if h had not been born." (14:17–14:21)

they were eating, Jesus took bread, and when he had blessed, he broke
gave it to them, and said, "Take, eat. This is my body." He took the cup,
d when he had given thanks, he gave it to them. They all drank of it. He
id to them, "This is my blood of the new covenant, which is poured out for
ıny. I will no more drink of the fruit of the vine until that day when I drink
n the Kingdom of God." (14:22–14:25)

They went to the Mount of Olives and Jesus said, "All of you will stumb because of me tonight; for it is written, 'I will strike the shepherd, and t sheep will be scattered.' However, after I am raised up, I will go before y into Galilee." Peter said, "Perhaps others but not I." Jesus replied, "Ev this night, before the rooster crows twice, you will deny me three times." E Peter was adamant, "If I must die with you, I will not deny you." They all s the same thing. (14:26–14:31)

hey came to a place named Gethsemane. Jesus said to his disciples, "Sit ere while I pray." He took with him Peter, James, and John and became istressed. He said, "My soul is sorrowful. Stay here and watch." He went orward a little and fell on the ground and prayed that if it were possible, ie hour might pass away from him. He said, "Abba, Father, all things are ossible to you. Please remove this cup from me. However, not what I desire ut what you desire." (14:32–14:36)

Jesus returned to find them sleeping and said to Peter, "Are you sleeping
Couldn't you watch one hour? Watch and pray that you may not enter int
temptation. The spirit is willing, but the flesh is weak." Again, he went an
prayed the same words. Again, he returned and found them sleeping. H
came the third time and said to them, "The hour has come. Behold, the Sc
of Man is betrayed into the hands of sinners. Let us be going. Behold, h
who betrays me is at hand." (14:37–14:42)

Now, Judas had told the Pharisees, scribes and elders, "Whomever I kiss, that is Jesus. Seize him and lead him away safely." When he had come, immediately, he came to Jesus, saying, "Rabbi! Rabbi!" and kissed him. Then soldiers laid their hands on Jesus and seized him. One of the disciples drew his sword and struck the servant of the high priest and cut off his ear. (14:43–14:47)

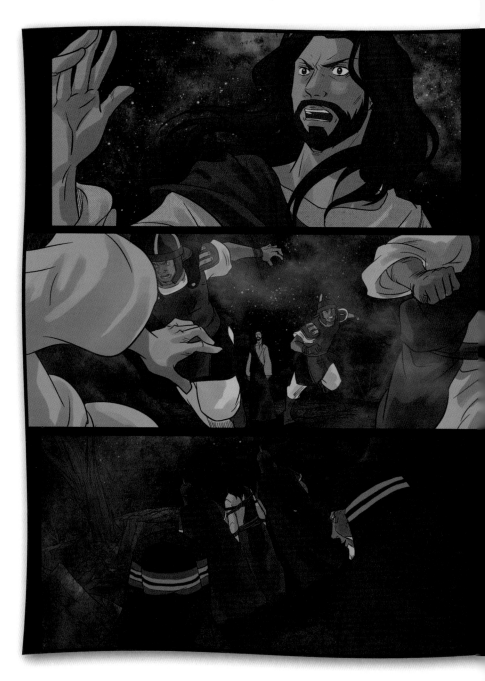

Jesus spoke out, "Have you come out as against a robber with swords a[nd] clubs to seize me? I was with you in the temple teaching, and you did [not] arrest me. But this is so that the Scriptures might be fulfilled." The disciples [all] left him and fled. The soldiers led Jesus away to the high priest. All the ch[ief] priests, the elders, and the scribes came together with him. (14:48–14:5[3])

...ter followed at a distance, watching as the high priest and council sought ...itnesses against Jesus to put him to death. But though many gave false ...stimony against him, their testimony didn't agree. Some stood up, saying, ...Ne heard him say, 'I will destroy this temple that is made with hands, and ...three days, I will build another made without hands.'" Even so, their ...stimony did not agree. (14:54–14:59)

The high priest stood up in the midst and asked Jesus, "Have you no answer What is it which these testify against you?" But Jesus stayed quiet and answered nothing. Again, the high priest asked him, "Are you the Chris the Son of the Blessed?" Jesus said, "I am. You will see the Son of Ma sitting at the right hand of Power and coming with the clouds of the sky. (14:60–14:62)

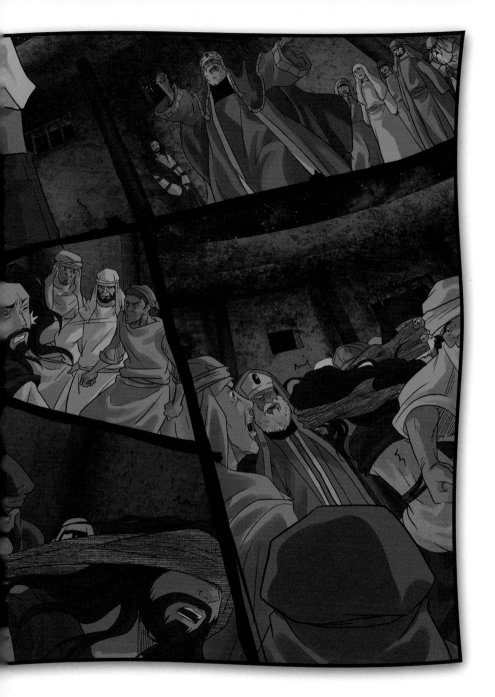

e high priest tore at his clothes, "What further need have we of witnesses? u have heard the blasphemy! What do you think?" They all condemned m to be worthy of death. Some began to spit on him and to cover his face d to beat him with fists and to tell him, "Prophesy!" The officers struck him th the palms of their hands. (14:63–14:65)

One of the high priest's maids saw Peter, and said, "You were with Nazarene, Jesus!" But he denied it. He went out on the porch, and rooster crowed. The maid called out, "He is one of them." But Peter ag denied it. But others said, "You are one of them; for you are a Galilea Peter began to swear, "I don't know this man!" The rooster crowed ag and Peter remembered, "Before the rooster crows twice, you will deny three times," and he wept. (14:66–14:72)

the morning, the chief priests, elders, scribes, and the council bound
Jesus and delivered him up to Pilate. Pilate asked him, "Are you the King of
the Jews?" Jesus answered, "So you say." The chief priests accused him of
many things. Pilate again asked him, "Have you no answer? See how many
things they testify against you!" But Jesus made no further answer, and Pilate
marveled. (15:1–15:5)

Now, at the feast, Pilate traditionally released to the people one prisoner whom they asked of him. There was one called Barabbas bound with those who had committed murder. The multitude cried out for Pilate to release a prisoner. He answered them, saying, "Do you want me to release to you the King of the Jews?" For he perceived that for envy, the chief priests had delivered him up. (15:6–15:10)

But the chief priests convinced the people to call for Barabbas. Pilate again asked what he should do with Jesus, "Crucify him!" Pilate pleaded, "Why, what evil has he done?" Still they cried, "Crucify him!" Pilate, wishing to please the multitude, released Barabbas and had Jesus flogged. The soldiers then prepared him for crucifixion, clothing him in purple with a crown of thorns on his head. (15:11–15:17)

They saluted him, "Hail, King of the Jews!" They struck his head with a reed and spat on him and mocked him. They took the purple robe off him and led him out to be crucified. They compelled a man from the country, Simon of Cyrene, to help bear his cross. Finally, they brought Jesus to the place called Golgotha, "the place of a skull." They offered him wine mixed with myrrh to drink, but he didn't take it. (15:18–15:23)

Three hours after the start, they crucified him and cast lots for his garments. Above his head, they wrote: "THE KING OF THE JEWS." They also crucified two robbers. The Scripture was fulfilled, which says, "He was numbered with transgressors." Those who passed by blasphemed Jesus, saying, "Ha! You who would destroy the temple and rebuild it in three days, save yourself and come down from the cross!" (15:24–15:30)

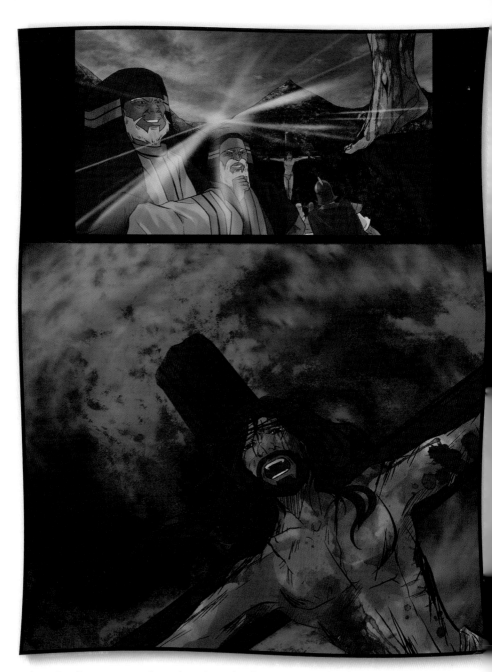

The chief priests and scribes laughed, "He saved others, but let the Chris[t,] the King of Israel, come down from the cross that we may see and believ[e] him." Those who were crucified with Jesus insulted him. From the sixth hou[r] on, there was darkness over the whole land until the ninth hour. At the nint[h] hour, Jesus cried with a loud voice, "My God, my God, why have yo[u] forsaken me?" (15:31–15:34)

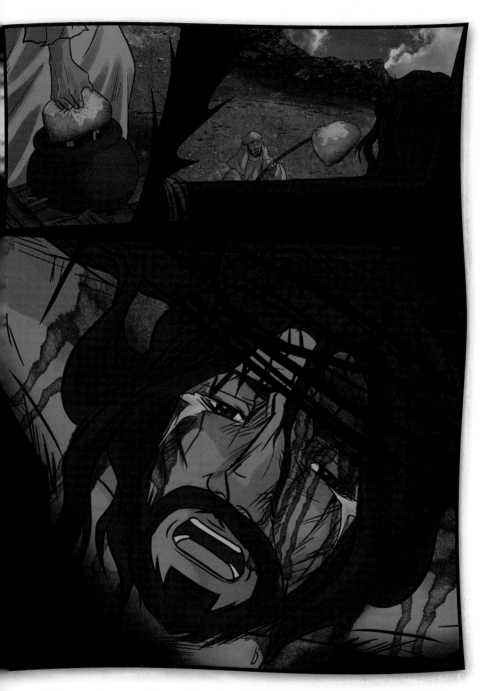

ome of those who stood by, when they heard it, said, "Behold, he is calling
ijah." One ran, and filling a sponge full of vinegar, put it on a reed and
ave it to him to drink, saying, "Let's see whether Elijah comes to take him
own." Jesus cried out with a loud voice. (15:35–15:37)

And Jesus gave up his spirit. (15:37)

The veil of the temple was torn in two from the top to the bottom. The centurion who stood by said, "Truly, this man was the Son of God!" (15:38–15:39)

There were women watching who had come to Jerusalem with Jesus including Mary Magdalene and Mary, the mother of James, Joses, and Salome. That evening, because it was the day before the Sabbath, Joseph of Arimathaea, a prominent council member who also himself was looking for the Kingdom of God, came. He boldly went in to Pilate and asked for Jesus' body. (15:40–15:43)

ilate, summoning the centurion, asked him whether he had been dead long. Vhen he found out from the centurion, he granted the body to Joseph. oseph bought a sheet and, taking him down, wound him in the linen cloth nd laid him in a tomb that had been cut out of a rock. He rolled a stone gainst the door of the tomb. Mary Magdalene and Mary, the mother of ses, saw where he was laid. (15:44–15:47)

When the Sabbath was past, Mary Magdalene and Mary, the mother of James, bought spices that they might come and anoint him. Very early on the first day of the week, they came to the tomb. They were saying among themselves, "Who will roll away the stone from the door of the tomb for us," for it was very big. Looking up, they saw that the stone was rolled back. (16:1–16:4)

Entering into the tomb, they saw a young man sitting on the right side dressed in a white robe. He said to them, "Don't be amazed. You seek Jesus who has been crucified. He has risen. He is not here. But go; tell his disciples and Peter, 'He goes before you into Galilee. There you will see him, as he said to you.'" They fled from the tomb trembling and said nothing to anyone; for they were afraid. (16:5–16:8)

Jesus appeared first to Mary Magdalene, from whom he had cast out seven demons. She went and told those who had been with him as they mourned, but they did not believe her. Jesus was then revealed in another form to two of them as they walked on their way into the country. They went away and told it to the rest, but they didn't believe either. (16:9–16:13)

Jesus then revealed himself to the eleven disciples, rebuking them for not believing those who had seen him first. He said, "Go into all the world and preach the Good News to all. He who believes and is baptized will be saved, but he who disbelieves will be condemned. These signs will accompany those who believe: in my name they will cast out demons." (16:14–16:17)

"They will speak with new languages; they will take up serpents, and
they drink any deadly thing, it will not hurt them; they will lay hands on th
sick who will recover." So then the Lord, after he had spoken to them, wc
received up into heaven and sat down at the right hand of God. They we
and preached, the Lord working with them and confirming the word by th
signs that followed. Amen. (16:17–16:20)

MAP

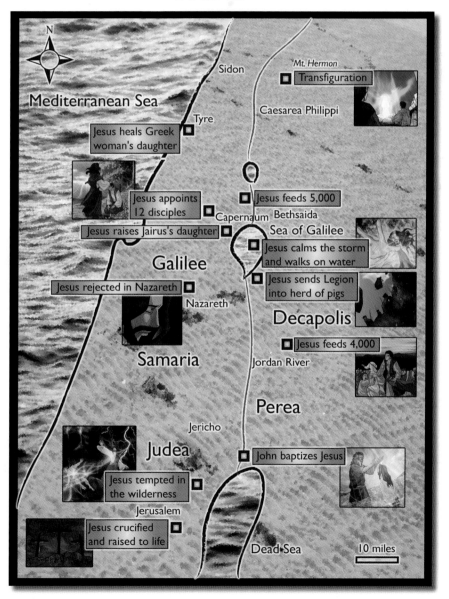

MAP OF JERUSALEM

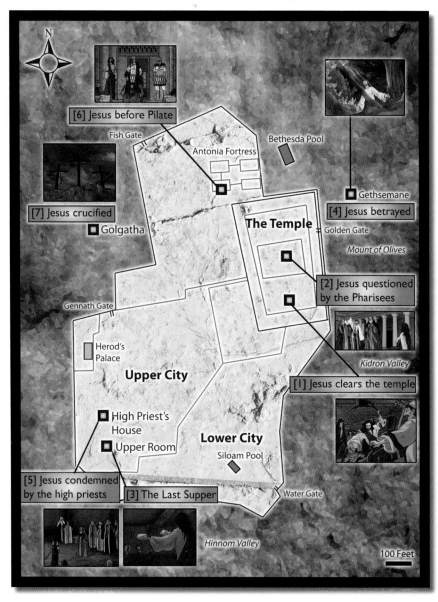

N

[6] Jesus before Pilate

Fish Gate

Bethesda Pool

Antonia Fortress

Gethsemane

[7] Jesus crucified

[4] Jesus betrayed

Golgatha

The Temple

Golden Gate

Mount of Olives

[2] Jesus questioned by the Pharisees

Gennath Gate

Herod's Palace

Kidron Valley

Upper City

[1] Jesus clears the temple

High Priest's House

Upper Room

Lower City

Siloam Pool

[5] Jesus condemned by the high priests

[3] The Last Supper

Water Gate

Hinnom Valley

100 Feet